Helping Hands

I picked up my clothes;
I swept the floor;
I took out the trash;
I held the door.

I came when Mom called;
I said, "Yes, please";
I cleaned up my plate;
I ate those peas.

I told Mom "Good night";
I heard her say,
"How happy you've been,
All smiles all day."

So my helping hands
Helped Mom, you see;
But now I know they
Really helped me.
~Dawn L. Watkins

Reading 1C   Third Edition

bju press®

Greenville, South Carolina

T his textbook was written by members of the faculty and staff of Bob Jones University. Standing for the "old-time religion" and the absolute authority of the Bible since 1927, Bob Jones University is the world's leading fundamental Christian university. The staff of the University is devoted to educating Christian men and women to be servants of Jesus Christ in all walks of life.

Providing unparalleled academic excellence, Bob Jones University offers over 60 undergraduate programs with dozens of concentrations and over 30 graduate programs, while its fervent spiritual emphasis prepares the minds and hearts of students for service and devotion to the Lord Jesus Christ.

▶ If you would like more information about the spiritual and academic opportunities available at Bob Jones University, please call *1-800-BJ-AND-ME (1-800-252-6363)*. *www.bju.edu*

NOTE:
The fact that materials produced by other publishers may be referred to in this volume does not constitute an endorsement of the content or theological position of materials produced by such publishers. Any references and ancillary materials are listed as an aid to the student or the teacher and in an attempt to maintain the accepted academic standards of the publishing industry.

READING 1C
Helping Hands
Third Edition

Coordinating Authors	**Designers**	**Composition**
Susan J. Lehman	Holly Gilbert	Carol Larson
Linda O. Parker	David Siglin	
		Photo Acquisition
Editor	**Cover**	Carla Thomas
Debbie L. Parker	Elly Kalagayan	
Project Manager		
Victor Ludlum		

Acknowledgments and Photo Credits are listed on page 151.

© 2005 BJU Press
Greenville, South Carolina 29614
First Edition © 1981 BJU Press
Second Edition © 1989 BJU Press

ISBN 978-1-59166-269-3
ISBN 978-1-59166-455-0 (READING 1A–1F Set)

15 14 13 12 11 10

Contents
Helping Hands

If Everybody Did

From the book *If Everybody Did*
Written and illustrated by Jo Ann Stover

When there's only one, that's just SOMEBODY. . . .

But when there's one... and one... and one.... and more......
that's EVERYBODY.

Did you ever think of
what would happen if
EVERYBODY did
things like......

Make tracks?

This is what would happen if Everybody did

Spill tacks ?

this is what would happen if Everybody did

Pull off a bud?

this is what would happen if Everybody did

Jump in the mud ?

this is what would happen if Everybody did

SQUEEZE THE CAT?

THIS IS WHAT WOULD HAPPEN IF EVERYBODY DID

Forget your hat?

this is what would happen if EVERYBODY did

Put toys on the stair ?

This is what would happen if Everybody did

hop over the chair ?

This is what would happen if Everybody did

Drop your cup?

This is what would happen if Everybody did

Stay up?

This is what would happen if Everybody did

But when there's.....

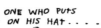

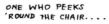

ONE WHO LEAVES
NO TRACKS......

ONE WHO DOESN'T
USE TACKS......

ONE WHO
SMELLS A BUD....

ONE WHO STEPS
OVER THE MUD....

ONE WHO
PATS THE CAT.....

ONE WHO PUTS
ON HIS HAT....

ONE WHO TAKES
TOYS OFF
THE STAIR.....

ONE WHO PEEKS
'ROUND THE CHAIR....

12

ONE WHO SETS DOWN HIS CUP. . . .

ONE WHO DOESN'T STAY UP. . . . .

WHY, THAT'S EVERYBODY!   AND....

THIS IS WHAT WOULD HAPPEN IF EVERYBODY DID

Marta's Blessing

Addy Forrest
illustrated by Keith Neely

Mopping and Dusting

Marta was sad.
Marta had asked to swim with Ashley.
But Mamá said, "Mrs. Wade's mother is
in the hospital.
I have a job for us to do.
You and I will help her with her work."

"I do not want to help," Marta was thinking.
"I would rather be a splashing, swishing fish."
Marta did not chat with Mamá in the van.

But Mamá and Marta got to work.
Mamá swept the steps, and Marta
picked up trash.
Mamá mopped the floor, and Marta
scrubbed the tub.
Mamá made the beds, and Marta
dusted the dressers.

16

Marta splashed the dishwater at Mamá.
Mamá and Marta giggled.
They had fun.

Marta wanted to be splashing with Ashley.
But Marta was glad Mrs. Wade would get
a surprise.

Hugs and Smiles

At last the work was finished.
The mess was picked up.
Everything smelled fresh.

Just then Marta heard Mr. Wade's truck.

Mr. Wade held the door.
"Who swept the floor?" Mr. Wade said.

"Where are the dishes?" Mrs. Wade said.
"You have done a lot of work!"

Mrs. Wade's eyes were wet.

Mrs. Wade gripped Mamá's hand.
"Thank you for your work!"

Marta got a big hug from Mrs. Wade.
"You are a blessing," Mr. Wade said.

Mamá and Marta went to the van.

Marta asked Mamá, "Can you and I do any other work for Mrs. Wade?"

Mamá said, "But would you rather swim with Ashley? I will let you."

"It is fun to swim, but it is fun to help," said Marta. "I was selfish. Will you forgive me?"

Mamá gave Marta a big smile.
"Yes," Mamá said, "I forgive you."

Marta and Mamá chatted in the van.

"I like to splash and swish like a fish,"
said Marta. "But when I help, I am a
blessing."

At Home in Color

Dawn L. Watkins
illustrated by Julie Speer

Homesick for Color

Once upon a time in Smoke Grove,
grass was not green.
It was black.
The rose was not red.
It was white with a white stem.
Grapes were black with white stripes.
Everything in Smoke Grove was black
and white.

Once when the sun shone well,
Otter went off to swim.

"I heard something," Otter said to
himself.

A pebble plopped into the water.

"Who is there?" asked Otter.

"I'm here," said Pig, "alone."

"Pig! I am glad you are here.
Do you want to swim?" asked Otter.

Pig sniffed and then gave a little sob.

Otter dove off the bank. "What is the matter?"

Pig said, "I am homesick!"

"Homesick?" asked Otter.
"But everybody likes it here."

Pig dabbed his nose. "I miss color."

"Is Color someone in your family?" asked Otter.

"Color is not a someone.
Color is blue and yellow and purple.
Where I come from, things are in color, not just black and white," Pig sobbed.

Otter gasped. "Do tell!"

Does Color Matter?

Otter got everyone in the Grove to come hear Pig tell his tale.

"Yes," said Pig. "Back home a rose is red.
Sometimes pink.
Grass is green.
Grapes are purple.
Everything is pretty."

"You did not tell us," said Frog.

"It was rude," said Pig.
"I could not tell you your home was not pretty!"

"What color are crickets at your home?" asked Cricket.

"They are black.
But foxes are brown.
And frogs are green," said Pig.

There was a buzz then.
Everybody wanted to hear what color things were.

"Let us get color here," said Otter.

Fox said, "Everybody is used to black and white.
Color does not matter to us."

But Fox was a blacksmith who was used to smoke and black dust.

"Yes! Color," said everyone but Fox.

Pig said, "Color just is.
I do not think I can make it for you."

"You must help us," said Otter.
"Help us find a cure for black and white!"

Pig shrugged. "I cannot do that."

"Come on, Pig," said Otter.
"If you help us get color, it will help you.
You will not get homesick!"

Pig nodded and then broke into a big
smile.

The Color Cure

"A gemstone!" Pig said.
"Get a pure gemstone."

Otter went home and got his big white gemstone.
"You can use this," Otter said.

"I must crush your pretty stone," said Pig.

Otter nodded. "If it will help us get color, then you can crush it."

Pig crushed the gemstone to pure dust.
"Bring pots," Pig said.
"Let us mix the dust with water from the lake."

And when Otter did that, everyone gasped.
The water was blue,
then green,
then purple,
then pink,
then orange,
then back to blue.

"This is watercolor!" said Pig.
"Get brushes, everyone!"

29

Otter got everyone brushes.

Cricket brushed the grass green.
Pig brushed the rose red.
Frog brushed the grapes purple.

Otter brushed Fox brown.
But the tip of his nose was still black.

They brushed and brushed.
Smoke Grove got color with every stroke.

Then Pig said, "This is not Smoke Grove.
This is Color Cove!"

And it was Color Cove for the rest of time.

Color Cove

Black and White

Suppose everything in your bedroom was black and white. Use your black crayon to draw a picture of your bedroom.

Write a sentence about your picture of your bedroom.

I like my trains.

The Big, Black, Thumping Tadpole

Candy Jamison
illustrated by Dana Thompson

The Picnic

June passed at last.
It was time for the big picnic.
Mike and Brent ran to the picnic spot.
A big, black thing came from the sun.
Mike and Brent stopped.

"What is that thing?" asked Mike.

"It is a big, black, thumping tadpole!"
yelled Brent.

"Fiddlesticks!" said Mike.

"Well, it is big, black, and thumping,"
said Brent.
"And it is shaped like a tadpole."

"It is a helicopter," said Mike.
"And here it comes!"

The helicopter landed next to the picnic
spot.
A man jumped from the helicopter and
put up a red and yellow banner.
Then the man yelled, "Helicopter rides!
Just five dollars a ride!"

"Come on!" said Brent.

"But I have to help Uncle Luke set up," said Mike.

"You can do it some other time," said Brent.

"I can't," said Mike.

Brent ran off, but Mike went to help his Uncle Luke.

Uncle Luke had many things to do.
Uncle Luke had Mike fill the glasses.
Mike filled the orange glasses
and the green glasses,
the yellow glasses,
and the blue glasses.

As Mike filled the glasses, the helicopter
gave a ride.

When the glasses were full, Uncle Luke
had Mike set up the grill.
As Mike set up the grill, the helicopter
gave a ride.

Uncle Luke had Mike get some things
that they would use for the games.
As Mike worked, the helicopter gave ride
after ride.

The Finest Helper

Mike was hot and tired, but the jobs were finished.

Uncle Luke handed him five dollars. "That is for the finest helper at the picnic," said Uncle Luke.

Then Uncle Luke winked. "And you can have that helicopter ride you wanted."

"Thank you, Uncle Luke!" said Mike.

Mike dashed up to the helicopter.
Mike handed the money to the smiling
man.
The man helped Mike into the helicopter.
Then the man sat next to Mike in the
helicopter.

Mike waved to Uncle Luke.
Then the man gave the stick a pull, and
the helicopter went up.
The picnic spot shrank.
It got as little as an anthill.
The hilltop spun away from Mike.

"Do you want a faster ride?" asked the man.

"Yes!" Mike said.

The man gave the stick a twist, and the helicopter went faster.

Mike hoped the ride would not end.

"You are a brave rider," said the man.
"But it is time to land."

The helicopter landed back at the picnic spot.
Mike jumped from the helicopter and rushed up to Uncle Luke.

"Thank you!" Mike said.

Uncle Luke just winked.

A Different Look

Pretend that you are riding in a helicopter.
Circle each picture that shows the way things
would look when you are in the flying helicopter.

good work

1.

2.

3.

Helicopter Helpers

Milly Howard
illustrated by Jim Hargis

Helicopters can help people do many things.

This helicopter lifts up and up.
It is a traffic helicopter.
A man in the helicopter tells where the traffic jams are.
The man can tell people a better path to take. Then people can get to their jobs on time.

A rescue helicopter can get into spots
where others cannot.
When the water rises, this helicopter can
get to people who are stranded.
When someone must have help fast, the
helicopter can get there.
When a plane crashes in the hills, the
helicopter can take the people for help.

A combat helicopter takes people into
battle.
Then it brings them back.
The men in this helicopter can drop
things to help in the battle.

Helicopters help people do many brave
things.

Eyes in the Sky

Read the story.

This is a police helicopter.
It can help track a robber who is running away.
It can tell policemen where the robber is.
Then the policeman can get the robber.

Color the bubble next to the correct answer.

1. What kind of helicopter helps policemen?

    police ●   ○ traffic

2. What can a police helicopter track?
    ○ a policeman   ● a robber

A Brave Father

A true story by Major White with Eileen M. Berry
illustrated by John Roberts

Major White's Trip

The U.S. was at war with Iraq.
Major White was getting packed to help
in the war.

Major White wanted to spend time with
his wife and his son, Kris.
Kris and his dad sat on the steps.

"I love you, Dad," said Kris.

"And I love you, Kris," said Major White.

Kris and his mother were sad.

Major White had many men who worked
for him.
They had jobs to do in the war.
Major White and his men got on a big
plane.
Many of the men had time to take a nap
on the plane.

The plane landed at the base in Qatar.
It was time to get to work.
There were planes to fix.

Major White helped his men check the planes.
Major White gave his men the things they had to have to do their jobs.

Major White missed his wife and son.
But there were times to chat with them.
When Kris was getting up at home, it
was past lunchtime for his dad in Qatar.

When it was lunchtime for Kris and his
mother, it was bedtime in Qatar.

Glad to Get Home

It was hot in Qatar.
There was sand everywhere.
Sometimes sand got in the men's eyes.
The sand felt like little pebbles hitting
their skin.
Sometimes it rained.
Sometimes there was thick fog.

Once, someone yelled, "Code Red!"

Major White and his men had to stop and
put on masks.
They waited.
But God kept them safe.
They were glad when it was time to take
off the masks.

The men wanted to go home.
But they wanted to do their jobs for
the U.S.
They just kept working.

At last, Major White said to his men,
"It is time to make the trip home."

They got back on the big plane.
The men were glad to go home.
Many of them had been homesick in
Qatar.
The plane landed.
Mrs. White and Kris were there.
Kris could not wait to hug his dad.

"Where is Dad?" Kris asked his mother.

"Dad will come," said Mrs. White.

Then Dad got off the plane.

Kris and his mother ran to him.
They gave him a big hug.
Kris was glad that his dad had helped
the U.S.

But Kris was glad to have his brave
father home.

55

Camp Sunrise

Addy Forrest
illustrated by Keith Neely

Homesick

The man at the desk checked his list.
"Tim will be in the Blue Buckskin cabin.
You will be in the Red Ranchers cabin."

Reggie felt sad.

He said to Dad, "I do not want to be in
the Red Ranchers cabin. I want to be in
Tim's cabin."

Dad said, "You must stay in the Red
Ranchers cabin. You will like the other
campers.
You will have fun."

Reggie did not think he would.

Mr. Nick came to get Reggie.
He had a big grin.

His crumpled hat said, "Red Ranchers."

"I'm glad you will be in the cabin with me.
We will have fun," the big man said.

Reggie did not think he would.

"There is a lot to do at camp.
We will get up at sunrise," Mr. Nick said.
"We will learn from the Bible.
Then we will wade in the lake and get
tadpoles."

Reggie did not want to wade in the lake.
Reggie wanted to run home.
He was homesick.

Fun with Friends

The next day Reggie got up at sunrise.
He went to the lake with Mr. Nick and
the other campers.

The beach was still and damp.
The campers sat on big rocks.
Mr. Nick had his Bible.

*From the rising of the sun unto the going down of the same the
LORD's name is to be praised.* —Psalm 113:3

Mr. Nick said, "God wants us to praise
Him.
When we whine and gripe, we do not
praise God."

Reggie felt bad.
He had whined to Dad.
He asked God to help him do better.

59

Reggie had a lot of fun at camp.
He made some friends.
He rode the water slide with his friend
Dale.
He went fishing with his friends Mike
and Ron.
He even got to sit next to Tim at the
campfire.
He was not homesick.

Mom and Dad came to pick Reggie up
when camp ended.
Reggie handed them the craft he had
made.
It was made with thin yellow sticks.
"What's this?" said Dad.
"It is a sunrise," Reggie said with a smile.
"It will remind me of the fun I had at
Camp Sunrise.
It will remind me to praise God from
sunrise to sunset."

Stone Soup

Retold as a play by Janet Snow
illustrated by Justin Gerard

Cast

Narrator

Peddler

Blacksmith

Shopkeeper

Miller

Shopkeeper's wife

Baker's wife

Baker

Act I

Narrator: A peddler led his mule pulling a wagon of pots into Rockville.

Peddler: Pots for sale! Pots for sale! Who will buy a shining black pot?

Blacksmith: Not I. I do not need a pot.

Shopkeeper: Be on your way. I have pots to sell in the shop here.

Peddler: Well then, is there a bed where I could sleep?

Miller: A bed? Not here. Be on your way.

Peddler: But could you give me something to eat?

Shopkeeper's wife: Eat? You cannot get something for free.

Peddler: Then I will just have to make some stone soup. At least I still have these three little stones.

Miller: Stone soup? What do you use to make that?

Shopkeeper's wife: Who could eat soup made from stones?

Peddler: It is simple to make.
The king himself likes to eat it!
Let me put some water in this kettle.
I will let you see me make it.

Blacksmith: You may use the blacksmith shop fire for your soup.

Peddler: Thank you, friend.
I have had to use these stones for a whole week.
The stone soup could be a little thin.
But one cannot use what one does not have.

Narrator: The peddler dropped the three little stones into the water.
Plop, plop, plop.
He mixed the water with a big tin dipper.

Act II

Narrator: The peddler had a sip from his dipper.

Peddler: Mmm. If I just had some beans.

Miller: Would you share your soup with me?
I have some beans I can give you.

Peddler: Thank you, friend.
Your gift will help the soup.

Narrator: The peddler cut up the beans and added them to the soup.
He mixed the soup again.

Shopkeeper: What does it taste like?

Peddler: Mmm. If I just had some carrots.
Carrots would give the soup some color.
But one cannot use what one does not have.

Shopkeeper's wife: We have some carrots.
I will get them.

Peddler: Thank you, friend.
The carrots add color to the soup.
With just a little meat, we would have a feast!

Blacksmith: I think I have some beef.
I can add that to the soup!

Peddler: Thank you, friend.

(Enter Baker and Baker's wife.)

Baker's wife: What do I smell?

Peddler: You smell soup.
   And this may be the best stone soup I
   have made.

Narrator: The peddler mixed the soup.
   Many people came to smell the soup.
   Everyone was thinking of things to add.

Miller: Here is some yellow cheese.

Shopkeeper's wife: And I have salt and
   pepper.

Narrator: The peddler added each of these
   and mixed the soup.
   He tasted it again.
   The people pressed closer to see into
   the kettle.

Peddler: This stone soup is fit for the king! If we had a little cream, even the king would want to eat supper with us.

Baker's wife: We have some cream left from the baking today.

Baker: I will get it.

Narrator: The baker ran for the cream. The cream was thick and rich. The peddler mixed the cream into the soup.

Act III

Peddler: The soup is finished!
Everyone bring a dish, and we will
feast.

Baker: Wait! I have made some hot buns.
We can eat them with the soup.

Peddler: Stone soup and hot buns are a
king's supper.

Narrator: When everyone had eaten, the
peddler lifted his stones from the pot.
He wiped them off.

Peddler: Thank you, friends. It is late.
I must be off.
I must hunt for somewhere to sleep.

Shopkeeper: Don't leave yet.
Please stay.

Blacksmith: You can stay with me.

Narrator: The peddler stayed.

Narrator: The next day he gave the miller his three little stones.

Peddler: These are for the people of Rockville.
If you are hungry again, just use these stones.

Miller: *(looking at the stones)* I will, friend, I will.

Narrator: As the peddler went on his way, his smile was as wide as the lid of his kettle.

A Snowy Day
on Green Street

Addy Forrest
illustrated by Julie Speer

A Snowy Day

Mr. Simms sets the mail into his truck.
He is dressed in his thick blue jacket and
warm hat.
The sleet is freezing as it hits his cheeks.
But he has a job to do.

He steps on the gas, but the tires just dig
deeper.
He tramps to the back of the truck.
A snowdrift is stopping the tires.
Mr. Simms scrapes the snow away.

As Mr. Simms drives onto Green Street, the mail truck slides.

The street is slick.

Mr. Simms is glad the truck does not get stuck.

He has a big job.

The people on this street need to get their mail.

Mr. Simms is glad to take mail to the people.

He will put the mail in each mailbox.

Mr. Simms thinks of his home.
On freezing days, he wishes he could stay inside!
He would like to sip a hot drink and sit at the fire.
But he must take the mail to his friends on Green Street!

A Warm Heart

The mail truck creeps on the slick street.
It is taking a lot of time to take the mail
today.
But the people will be happy to get their
mail.

Kenny Bopp at 102 gets a big brown box
from Grandma.

Mrs. French at 104 gets six Christmas
cards.

Mr. Fisher at 106 is waiting at the door
for Mr. Simms.
He likes to get mail, but there is no mail
for him today.
Mr. Simms waves and smiles as
he passes Mr. Fisher.

From: Grandma

To: Kenny Bopp
102 Green Street
Springfield, PA 19064

Mrs. Betty French
104 Green Street
Springfield, PA 19

The red flag is up at 108.
The Creel family has mail for Mr. Simms
to pick up.
Mr. Simms feels inside the box.
There is some jam and a Christmas card
for "Mr. Simms."
Mr. Simms chuckles.
Well, I did not think I would get mail today!
He reads the card.

To Mr. Simms,
Here is some jam for you.
Thank you for bringing the mail
every day.
Love,
Jenny Creel

Mr. Simms

Mr. Simms smiles at the note.
His eyes twinkle.
I have never been thanked for bringing the mail!

He tucks the card and the jam in his pocket.

He is happy to take people their mail.

He pats the card and jam in his pocket.

Someone is thankful for the job he does every day.
And that makes him feel warm inside.

Little Letter

Use the words in the box to complete
the letter.

game   May   played

Dear Grandma,

Thank you for the _game_.

I have _played_ it every day.

Mom said that you will come to see us

in _May_. I am glad!

Love,
Kenny

A Christmas Song

Karen Wilt
illustrated by Preston Gravely Jr.

The Organ

"Thank you for coming, Mr. Gruber.
We need your help," said Preacher Mohr.
"I hope you can fix the organ in time to
play it on Christmas Eve."

"I was glad to come," said Mr. Gruber.
"I will see what I can do."

Preacher Mohr put on his warm hat and
mittens.
"I want to spend time with a family.
The mother just had a baby.
I will come back."

The hills were white and pretty, but the preacher did not see them.
The wind was chilly, but the preacher did not feel it.
He was sad.
The organ did not work.
It was Christmas Eve, and there would not be any singing.

The father and mother were glad the
preacher had come.
Preacher Mohr held their little baby and
prayed with them.
"Thank you, God, for this baby.
And thank you for the baby Jesus that
you sent to us."
As the preacher left, he thought of the
little baby he had held.
He thought of baby Jesus and Christmas.

The Preacher's Poem

Preacher Mohr went to his desk.
He thought of a silent Christmas Eve.
"Silent!" the preacher said to himself.
"I think I can do something!"
He picked up a pen.

Mr. Gruber came in to see him.
"The organ still does not work," he said.
"Why are you smiling?"

"I have a poem," the preacher said.
"The little baby I held made me think of Christ.
My poem tells of His coming.
Will you put a tune with it?"

"I like this poem," said Mr. Gruber.
"I will put a tune with your poem."

"And we will sing this song for Christmas.
We will not need the organ," said Preacher
Mohr.

A Song From God

Many weeks later, Preacher Mohr was at his desk again.

Mr. Gruber came to see him.

"A man has come to fix the organ," he said.

"Come, I will play the Christmas song."

Mr. Gruber played the song.
The man who fixed the organ stayed to hear.

"'Silent Night,' what a pretty song!" the man said.

"May I play 'Silent Night' for others?"

The man went home.
He gave the song to a family.
The children loved the song.
They sang it every day.
One day someone heard the song and
went to tell the king and queen.

The king and queen asked the children to come and sing for them.
"Sing for the king and queen?" asked the children.
"We will do it!" said the mother.

The children sang for the king and queen.

"Such a pretty song!" said the queen.
"That is a song from God," said the king.

Today many children in many lands sing this sweet song every Christmas.
It is one of the best songs to tell children of the coming of baby Jesus.

My Gift

Christina Rossetti
illustrated by Kathy Pflug

All
What can I give Him
Poor as I am;

Child 1
If I were a shepherd
I would give Him a lamb.

Child 2
If I were a wise man,
I would do my part.

All
But what can I give Him?

Child 3
I will give my heart.

89

Trust in God

Karen Wilt
illustrated by Dana Thompson

Plink, plunk went the cups on the plates.
Patty's cup was empty, and Patty's plate
was empty.

Mr. Mueller said, "We will pray to God.
We will trust Him to feed us."

Squeak, creak went something in the street.

Patty got up to see.

"I see someone," Patty said.
"A man has come to visit us.
It is a baker, and he has something in his hands."

"I could not sleep," the baker said to
Mr. Mueller.
"I made these for you to eat."

"Thank God!" said Mr. Mueller.
"He gave us something to eat."

Mr. Mueller helped the baker take the
buns inside.
Patty put a bun on each plate.
But the cups were still empty.

Clink, clank went something in the street.
Patty ran to see.
A milkman was waiting on the steps.

"I cannot drive this wagon," he said.
"I need to fix it.
Will you please take the milk?"

"Yes, we will be happy to take the milk,"
said Mr. Mueller.
"And we thank God for this meal."

The buns were warm, and the milk was sweet.
They ate, and they drank.
Then plink, plunk went the cups back onto the plates.

"It is time to clean up," said Patty.
"I am glad God gives us each thing that we need."

Ask, and it shall be given you. —Matthew 7:7

Firefighters

Nancy Lohr

A fireman rushes to a fire on a fast fire truck.

He may ride in the cab.

He might ride on the side.

The ladder truck is the biggest truck.

It needs two drivers.

One man drives the front.

One man drives the back.

The driver in front might turn to the right.

Then the driver in back must turn to the left.

The ladder can stand upright on top of the truck.
The firefighter will tie tight ropes to the ladder to make it safe.
Then the firefighter can go high into the sky.
He can fight the fire from the top.
He may shine a spotlight from the top of the ladder.

The pumper truck pumps water from a
hose.
The nozzle can let the water gush,
and it can make a light mist.
The firefighter might need to cut a hole
with his ax to get inside to the fire.
He will think of the best way to get water
on the fire.

The fireman must have a tight mask.
A mask will keep him safe from the thick
smoke and hot steam.
He will need the right hat and coat to
keep himself dry.
The fireman needs light at nighttime to
see well.
He may use a flashlight.

The fireman's job is not done when he comes back from a fire.
After each fire, he must clean the trucks.
He puts the trucks on the driveway.
He scrubs the trucks.
He cleans the nozzles.
Then the trucks shine in the sunlight.

A firefighter will do the best he can to fight each fire.
He wants us to be safe.

The Best Dog Yet

Nancy Lohr

illustrated by Stephanie True

A Stray Puppy

"Is that puppy sick, Dad?" asked Mom.

"I do not think he is sick," said Dad. "But he is weak, and he is thin. He is soaked to the skin. One stray dog for us, Mom."

"We do not need such a dog," said Mom.

Dad petted the dog. It shivered.

"You are right," Dad said. "We do not need this dog, but he needs us. If you will get a dish of scraps, I will dry the little one off."

Many days came and went. The puppy got bigger and bigger. His coat became bright and shining. He ran and tumbled in the grass. He yipped at Mom. He yapped at Dad. At night, he slept on the rug by their bed.

Then one day Mom said, "This stray is a big dog. He needs a proper home. He needs a proper name."

"Well," said Dad. "I think he has a proper home. He can stay here. I like him, and I want him to be my dog. I will give him a name. Rusty. We will name him Rusty."

Rusty Helps

Rusty was a grand dog. He frisked by Mom each day. He played with Dad. He slept by the bed at night.

One night Rusty smelled smoke. He whined at Dad. He licked Dad on the hand. Dad groaned, but he did not wake.

Rusty yipped at Mom.

"Stop, Rusty!" she said. "It is nighttime. Go back to sleep."

Rusty tugged on her sleeve. Then Mom woke up.

"Dad! There is smoke in here! There must be a fire!"

Dad jumped up and ran to the door. It was hot. Dad went to the window. It would not lift up.

"Quick! The fire is getting hotter. Will we be locked in?" asked Mom.

"Not if I can raise this window. Help me lift it," he said.

But they could not lift the window. It was shut tight.

Then Rusty pulled Mom back from the window. He dashed for the windowpane. Dad could not stop him. Rusty jumped up into the glass pane. The glass shattered, and Rusty landed on the grass below the window.

Mom and Dad scrambled after him. They dropped onto the grass and ran from the fire. Then they went to hug Rusty.

"Thank you, Rusty," Mom was crying.

Rusty groaned. He had a big gash on his back. He was bleeding.

Dad sat next to the bleeding dog. He patted Rusty.

"You are a brave dog, Rusty," Dad said. "We will help you get well. You are the best stray dog yet!"

Dog Saves Man and Wife

Riverton, Mich.—Late Friday night, fire swept the home of Mr. and Mrs. Kenneth Bright at 205 Oak Street. Rusty, their dog, woke his masters. When they could not lift the window, Rusty jumped into the glass pane, shattering it. The Brights followed the brave dog to safety. Rusty was treated at Hopewell Vet Hospital.

Big and Brave

Color the bubble next to each word that describes the brave dog.

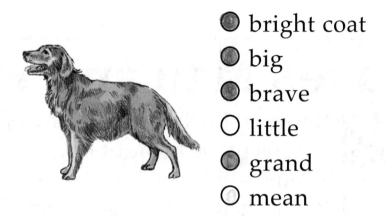

- ● bright coat
- ● big
- ● brave
- ○ little
- ● grand
- ○ mean

Make an award for the brave dog.

110

Zoo Camp

Kathleen Hynicka
illustrated by Keith Neely

Meeting Mr. Joe

The Miller van pulled up in front of Sandy Cove Zoo. Alex and Ashley could see the rest of the campers waiting on the benches by the front gate. They waved to Tim and Marta. Mr. Joe, the zookeeper, gave the campers a big smile as they ran to meet him.

"Who would like to help me feed the animals today?" asked Mr. Joe.

"We will!" Alex yelled.

"We were hoping we could be the feeding helpers today," said Ashley.

Mr. Joe pinned a yellow "Camp Pass" on Alex and Ashley. "These will show everybody that you are my helpers," he said as he led the way into the zoo.

"Is it fun to be a zookeeper?" asked Alex. He had to take big steps to keep up with Mr. Joe.

"Yes, being a zookeeper is fun," said Mr. Joe.

"But we are learning that it is a lot of work," said Alex.

"One day we gave water to many of the animals. It kept us working and working," said Ashley.

"And each one has to have a clean home," said Mr. Joe. "If an animal pen is not clean, I have to clean it."

"That is a big job," said Ashley. "You have a lot of animals here."

Mr. Joe nodded, "Yes, many animals live here at the zoo. That is why we have ten zookeepers. We work as a team. God gave us these animals. We want them to be at home here."

Fixing Lunch

Mr. Joe led Alex and Ashley to the zookeeper's hut. "I would like for you to put your lunches up on the shelf. Put them next to mine," said Mr. Joe. "Then you can come and help fix lunch for some of the animals. After the lunches are fixed, you can help feed the animals."

"See those pans on the shelf," said Mr. Joe. "Every day I fill those with fruit and grain. Each animal gets its own pan filled with what it likes to eat."

"Is that all they eat?" Ashley asked.

"Some animals get hay. We keep that in piles by their pens," Mr. Joe said.

"Today we need to fix lunch for Huey the elephant," said Mr. Joe. "He will be getting apples and hay."

"I like the elephant," Ashley said. "And Huey is a cute name."

"Who else will we feed?" Alex asked.

"The seals," Mr. Joe said. "We need to fill the pails under the shelf with fish for them."

It was a big job to wash apples for an elephant. Alex, Ashley, and Mr. Joe had to wash and wash. At last the pans were filled. Mr. Joe stepped back and said, "We are done. You two did a fine job. Huey will be happy to get this many apples. Next we need to fix the fish for the seals."

Mr. Joe went to get the big bags of fish. He put the bags of fish into the sink. Alex and Ashley dragged two pails over to the sink. Then they put the fish into the pails. The fish were not big, but they were wet. Alex and Ashley giggled every time one slipped from their hands.

"It is time to go feed Huey," Mr. Joe said when the pails were full.

Lunchtime

As they went up the path to the elephant pen, Ashley said, "Huey is such a big elephant. Do you think he will let us feed him?"

Mr. Joe nodded. "Yes," he said, "Huey may be big, but he is tame. He likes children, and he likes to eat apples. I will even show you what to do to make Huey do tricks."

When Mr. Joe held an apple up, Huey would bring his trunk up. Then he let Huey reach over with his trunk and take the apple from his hand. Next, Mr. Joe held an apple in front of him. He lifted one of his feet. Huey lifted one of his big feet. Again, Mr. Joe let Huey take the apple to eat.

Mr. Joe winked at Alex and Ashley. "I want to see each of you try," he said.

Alex got some apples to feed to the elephant. Each time he held an apple up, Huey would bring his trunk up. Alex would give him the apple.

Ashley held an apple for Huey to eat. Mr. Joe gave Huey a cue to lift one of his feet. Huey did it. Ashley gave Huey the apple.

Alex helped Mr. Joe give Huey his hay.

"We need to take the fish to the seals next," Mr. Joe said. "Miss Sue trains the seals. Pat and Pam, two of the seals, do a show at lunchtime. Miss Sue needs the fish for the show. She will feed them a fish every time they do a trick."

Alex and Ashley liked the seal show. Pat and Pam dove deep in the water. They jumped up to grab a pole. Miss Sue gave the seals a fish after each trick. For their last trick, Miss Sue had the seals give Alex and Ashley a kiss. Everybody clapped.

"What do we do next?" asked Alex as they went back to the zookeeper's hut.

Mr. Joe smiled. "It's lunchtime. But, no, I will not make you do a trick to get it!"

Lots of Lunches

Draw a line from each sentence to its matching picture.

They will put fish in the pails.

Mr. Joe held an apple for Huey.

Alex put his lunch on the shelf.

The Eagle and the Ant

A fable retold by Gail Fitzgerald
illustrated by Tim Davis

One fine day an ant was hot and dry.

"I see a stream. I will get a drink," said the ant. But the ant slipped and fell into the water. "Help! Help!" he yelled.

A big eagle sat in a tree close by. He let a stick drop into the stream. "Grab this stick," he said to the ant. "It will drift back to land."

"Thank you! You saved my life," said the ant to the eagle. "Maybe some day I can help you."

The ant spent many happy days by the stream. He and the eagle became great friends.

One day two men came to the stream. The ant felt the tromping of the men's feet on the land. Up in his tree the eagle did not feel the men's steps.

The men had guns. The eagle did not see the men and their guns. The ant did.

"Fly away, great friend," cried the ant. But the eagle did not hear the ant's cry.

One man stopped and aimed his gun. His finger was on the trigger, but he did not fire the gun. He dropped the gun and began to jump and scream. Then he sat on the grass and rubbed his leg.

"Why did you stop?" asked the other man.

"Something bit me," said his friend.

The ant was able to scramble from the man's sock. The ant went on his way with happy steps. He had been able to help his great friend.

Moral: One good deed deserves another.

Miriam Helps

Taken from Exodus 2:1–10
illustrated by Del Thompson

A Basket for Baby

"We cannot keep the baby here," said Father. "Someone will see him or hear him. Then the king's men will come to kill him, just as they killed many other sons."

"Then we will hide him in another spot," said Mother. "And God will keep the baby safe."

"I can weave a basket for the baby to lie in. We can let the basket float in the water. The basket will be safe in the reeds," Mother said.

"But will the baby be safe in the basket?" Miriam asked. "He can't swim."

"We can make a lid for the basket. We will tie the lid on so the baby will not tumble into the water," said Mother.

"Can I help?" Miriam wanted to keep her brother safe.

"You can come and help me cut the reeds," said Mother.

Father went to get some black, sticky stuff. He dipped it into a clay dish.

"I will rub this on the basket to keep it dry," he thought. "It will keep water from getting in."

Mother wove the reeds over and under, and Miriam helped. They made a tidy basket bed.

"See, Mother! The baby fits in his basket. He likes his cozy bed," Miriam said. "May I go with you to the stream?"

"Yes," said Mother. "We will take your brother where he will be safe from the king."

"The basket is a fine boat," said Mother. "See, it floats in the stream. It will not be seen in the reeds."

"I will stay close by," Miriam said. "I will hide and see what happens to him."

A Basket and a Princess

Miriam hid close to the floating basket. The basket bobbed on top of the water. It brushed by some reeds and swung close to the path by the water.

"Here comes someone!" Miriam thought. "It is the princess! Will she see the baby?"

The princess spoke to her maids. "Why is that basket in the reeds?"

"I will get it for you," said a maid. "And we can see what is in it."

The maid waded into the water. She came back, pulling the floating basket. She lifted the lid.

"It is a baby!" said the princess. "Why would anyone put a baby in the water?"

The baby began to cry.

"He is hungry," said the maid. "He needs to be fed."

Miriam came from her hiding spot in the reeds.

"I will get someone to feed the baby and watch after him," Miriam said to the princess.

Miriam ran to get her mother.

"I want to keep this baby," said the princess. "Will you feed him for me?"

"Yes," Mother said to the princess. "I will feed him. I will give him a home until he can live with you. I will treat him well."

Mother was glad to take the baby back to his home. She would feed him, and he would be safe from the king's men.

God had kept Moses safe, and Moses became God's man.

And the child grew, and she brought him unto Pharaoh's daughter, and he became her son. —Exodus 2:10

To Be Great

Eileen M. Berry
illustrated by David Schuppert

The Letter

President Lincoln sat at his desk thinking. He had a pile of letters in front of him. Many of the letters, like the one at the top of the stack, were on the war.

America had split into two sides. The two sides were fighting with each other, and many men had been killed. People were praying that the war would end. President Lincoln felt sad as he sat thinking.

The top letter on his stack was from a friend of his. The man's son, Jed, was in the war. Jed was just sixteen, but he had done something bad. He had run away from a battle. Soldiers who ran from battles were punished. Jed's father asked Lincoln to forgive his son and keep him from being punished.

President Lincoln wanted to do what was right. Jed had run from the battle, but he was just a lad.

The President had some sons of his own. He was thinking of what they would have done.

Just then the President's son, Tad, peeked in. "Pa," he said, "is it time to play yet?"

President Lincoln gazed at Tad and did not say a thing.

"Pa?" said Tad.

"We will play in a little while, Tad."

The Deal

The President picked up his pen.

"I will make a deal with Jed," he said. "I will forgive him, but he must go back to the battle. He must stay till the war is done. He must not run from a battle ever again."

The President penned a letter to Jed's leader. Then he put his name in big letters: "A. Lincoln."

Tad peeked in again. "Pa," he said, "is it time to play?"

President Lincoln smiled at Tad. "Yes, Tad," he said. "What game shall we play?"

"Let's play leapfrog!" Tad squealed.

The President set his pen aside and went to play with Tad.

For weeks and weeks the war went on. One day President Lincoln put on his hat. He said, "I will be back. I need to go to the hospital to visit the men who got shot in the war."

"May I come with you, Pa?" asked Tad. "Please?"

The President stopped at the door. "It will not be fun, Tad," he said. "Many are bleeding from gunshots. You will see men who are very sick."

"Please let me come, Pa," said Tad again.

"Well," the President said to himself, "maybe it will help the men to see Tad. Maybe he can make them smile."

He smiled at Tad. "You may come," he said. "But you must not run and play at the hospital. You must keep still and stay with me."

"I will," said Tad.

The Visit

At the hospital, the men were on the cots in rows. President Lincoln went from cot to cot. He held one man's hand. He spoke to another man quietly. He smiled at each one.

Tad stayed close to his father and kept still.

One soldier sat up when the President came to his cot. "Mr. President," he said.

"Yes?" President Lincoln smiled at him.

"My name is Jed. My father is your friend. He sent you a letter asking you to forgive me. If it were not for you, sir, I would have been punished weeks ago. I ran from a battle, but you forgave me. I went back to the fighting, sir, just like you said. I want to thank you, sir."

The President nodded. "It is I who must thank you. Thank you for fighting for us. What happened to you in the battle?"

"Got shot in my leg, sir. I was afraid, but I did not run."

The President bent to grip Jed's hand. "A brave soldier may be afraid, but he does not run."

"Is this your son, Mr. Lincoln?" asked Jed.

"Yes, this is Tad," said the President. Tad smiled at Jed.

Jed smiled back. "Pleased to meet you, Tad," he said. "Your father is a great man. You would do well to be like him some day."

President Lincoln spoke to his son. "Tad, it is a great thing to be President. And it is a great thing to be brave. Jed is a brave lad. You would do well to be like him."

"Thank you, sir." Jed's eyes were wet when the President and Tad left.

ABRAHAM LINCOLN,

Presidential People

Draw lines from each president to the matching coin and bill.

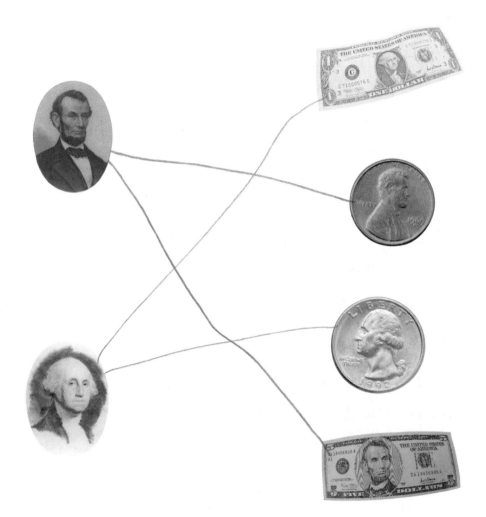

Glossary

A

an·i·mals

Cows and horses are farm animals.

B

beach

I found some shells on the beach.

Bi·ble

The Bible is God's Holy Word.

C

car·rots

Rabbits eat lettuce and carrots.

crick·ets

Crickets chirp in the evening.

D

dol·lar

Grandpa gave me a dollar to spend.

dove

Scott dove into the swimming pool.

E

el·e·phant

The big gray elephant has a long trunk.

eyes

Jill has brown hair and blue eyes.

F

fam·i·ly

There are two children in the family.

fire·fight·er

The firefighter sprayed water on the fire.

G

gash

The knife cut a gash in the car's tire.

gem·stone

Grandma's ring has a red gemstone.

grain

The farmer plants grain in his field.

grin

My grin shows all my teeth.

H

hel·i·cop·ter

The helicopter flew over the forest fire.

I

Iraq

Iraq is a country in the Middle East.

J

jack·et

Amy put on her warm jacket.

K

king

The king sits on his throne.

L

lamb

A lamb's wool is soft and curly.

Lin·coln

Lincoln was our sixteenth president.

M

mon·ey

Ann put her money in her piggy bank.

N

noz·zle

Water sprays out of the nozzle on the hose.

O

or·gan

Mr. Parker plays the organ at our church.

P

pock·et

Ben put his keys in his pocket.

Q

queen

The queen is wearing her crown.

R

S

shat·tered

The glass broke and shattered on the floor.

shep·herd

A shepherd cares for his sheep.

sol·dier

The soldier guarded the tank.

soup

Grandma makes good chicken soup.

swept

Dad swept the floor with a broom.

T

tad·pole

The tadpole will grow to be a frog.

trig·ger

The hunter pulled the trigger of his gun.

U

V

W

wade

Blake took off his shoes to wade
in the creek.

wag·on

Jen pulled the wagon down the sidewalk.

wash

We wash our dog when it gets dirty.

X

Y

Z

zoo

There is a white tiger in the zoo.

Acknowledgments

"If Everybody Did," by Jo Ann Stover, excerpted from *If Everybody Did*. Copyright © 1960 by Jo Ann Stover; David McKay Company, Inc., NY. Copyright © 1989 by Bob Jones University Press; Greenville, SC 29614. Used with permission.

Photo Credits

The following agencies and individuals have furnished materials to meet the photographic needs of this textbook. We wish to express our gratitude to them for their important contribution.

Suzanne Altizer
ATA Airlines, Inc.
John Bjerk
Corbis
Eastman Chemicals Division
Hemera Technologies
KME Fire Apparatus

Joyce Landis
Library of Congress
Susan Perry
PhotoDisc/Getty Images
Rebecca Schuppert
Carla Thomas
Unusual Films

"A Brave Father"
Used by permission of ATA Airlines, Inc. 49

"Firefighters"
KME Fire Apparatus 95; PhotoDisc/Getty Images 96; Eastman Chemicals Division of Eastman Kodak Company 97; Suzanne Altizer 98; Joyce Landis 99

"To Be Great"
Library of Congress 149, 150 (Abraham Lincoln, George Washington); © 2004 Hemera Technologies. All rights reserved. 150 (one dollar bill, five dollar bill); PhotoDisc/Getty Images 150 (penny, quarter)

Back Matter
PhotoDisc/Getty Images 153 (horses, cow, cricket), 154 (elephant), 155 (grain, grin), 156 (money), 157 (queen), 159 (wagon); Susan Perry 153 (Bible); Unusual Films 154 (family, firefighter), 157 (organ); Rebecca Schuppert 154 (dollar); Carla Thomas 155 (gemstone); Corbis 155 (helicopter); Joyce Landis 156 (jacket), 157 (nozzle); Library of Congress 156 (Abraham Lincoln); John Bjerk 159 (tadpole); © 2004 Hemera Technologies. All rights reserved. 159 (rifle)